D0718015

Some birds are
big,

some birds are small

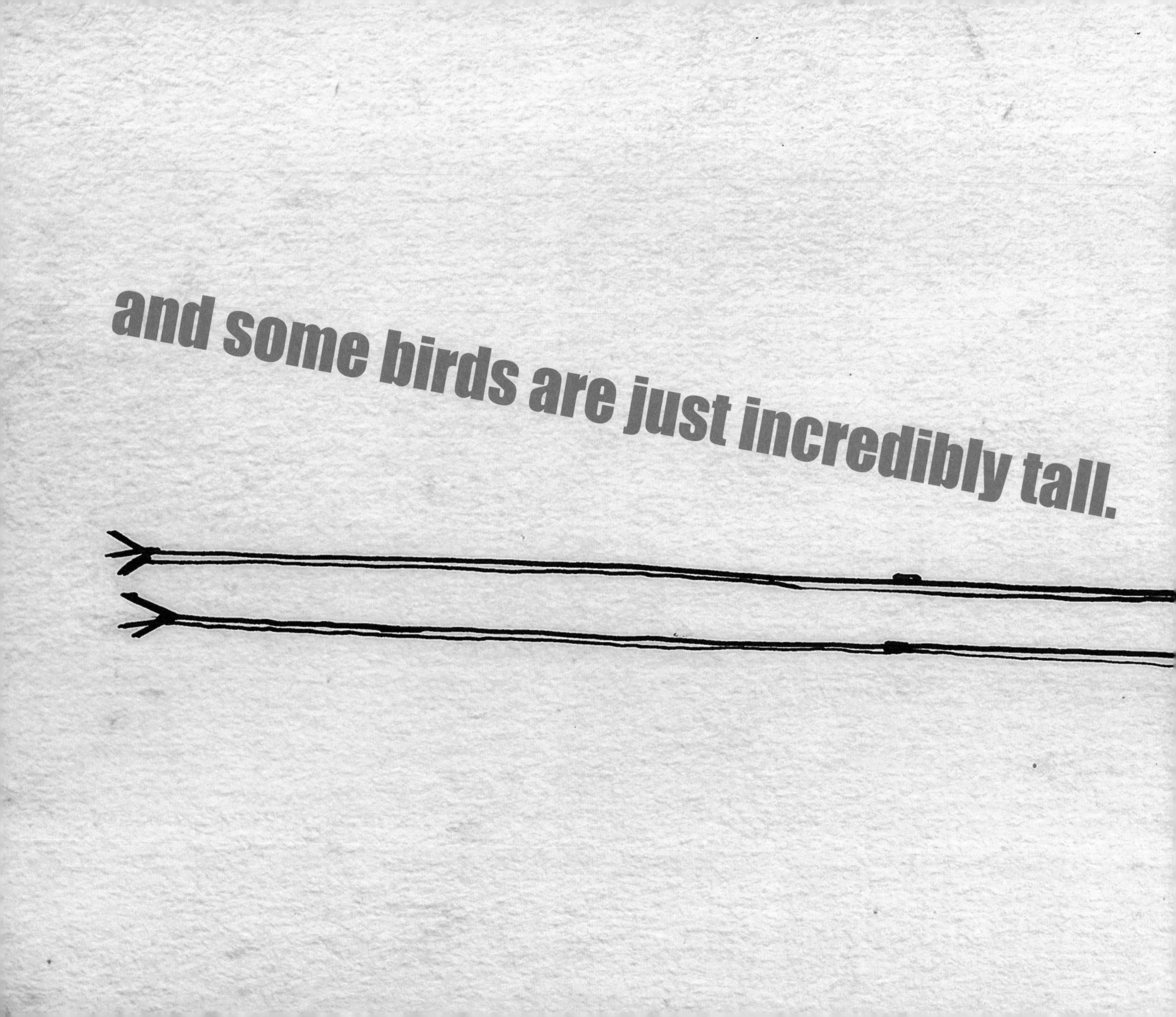
and some birds are just incredibly tall.

Some birds swoop

and some birds
squawk,

some birds soar high,

while some birds just

walk.

Some birds
waddle.

some birds hop

and some birds eat worms

until they go pop!

Some birds twitch,

some
birds
tweet

and some birds swim fast with

webbed flipper feet.

Some birds
flutter,

some birds
flap

and some birds fly off

to other parts of the map.

Some birds
build nests
away from
sly cats

and some birds make holes with a

rat-a-tat-
tat!

Some birds are caged,

but most birds are

FREE.

A much better life

I’m sure you’ll agree.